BEYOND CODING:

How ICD-10 Will Transform
Clinical Documentation

Charles L. Fred
Heather A. Haugen, PhD

Louann K. Reilly, Systems Thinking Analyst

Inbal C. Vuletich, Editor

MAGNUSSON
SKOR

Denver
www.magnussonskor.com

Published by

MAGNUSSON SKOR

Magnusson Skor Publishing
5690 DTC Boulevard
Greenwood Village, CO 80111
www.magnussonskor.com

To purchase Magnusson Skor products, please call (303) 483-4300 or visit www.magnussonskor.com.

Library of Congress Cataloging-in-Publication Data

Fred, Charles L.
Haugen, Heather A.
Reilly, Louann K.
Ed. Inbal Vuletich

First Edition

This book is dedicated to those committed to advancing the quality of healthcare through the effective adoption of Health Information Technologies.

iv

ACKNOWLEDGEMENTS

A book like this is not possible without the help of many other contributors. Our advisors and colleagues give tirelessly of their time, expertise, and counsel. They reinforce our belief that the transition from ICD-9 to ICD-10 is a real pain point in healthcare and is worthy of this publication.

David Beuther, Bill Spooner, Jill Truitt, Jon Melling and Liz Chapman each took extensive time to review the entire publication and provide specific recommendations for improvement, and we cannot thank them enough for their efforts on our behalf.

This book would not have been possible without Inbal Vuletich, our editor. Ms. Vuletich brings life to our prose and structure to our process. Her willingness to continually write, rewrite and edit our work is invaluable to our ongoing research efforts. We are indebted to her for her commitment to every last detail of this publication.

Our colleagues at The Breakaway Group provide deep healthcare experience and emotional support for our research and publications. Their commitment to our clients drives us to live our passion and give back to healthcare.

Greg Davis is our creative expert - from design to layout and printing. He is truly gifted in this area and we are thankful to have him on our team.

On a personal note, we are forever indebted to our spouses, children and friends who have encouraged us throughout the development of this book.

CONTENTS

BEYOND CODING:

How ICD-10 Will Transform Clinical Documentation

INTRODUCTION

2

> "*It was the best of times, it was the worst of times, it was the age of wisdom, it was the age of foolishness, it was the epoch of belief, it was the epoch of incredulity, it was the season of Light, it was the season of Darkness, it was the spring of hope, it was the winter of despair, we had everything before us, we had nothing before us, we were all going direct to heaven, we were all going direct the other way - in short, the period was so far like the present period, that some of its noisiest authorities insisted on its being received, for good or for evil, in the superlative degree of comparison only.*"

- Charles Dickens, *A Tale of Two Cities*

Fundamental change has arrived in healthcare, occupying center stage in our politically polarized world. Care providers who have dedicated their lives to helping others may feel that these are the worst of times as they struggle to adapt to new mandates. In fact, because healthcare is receiving new funding to update technologies, and because the national agenda continues to focus on issues driving the cost and quality of care, healthcare may actually be experiencing the best of times.

Our ongoing research shapes the pages of this book. Since 2007, we have conducted countless conversations with healthcare leaders that helped to frame our message. In 2010, in *Beyond Implementation: A Prescription for EMR Adoption,* we introduce a methodology for adoption of an Electronic Health Record (EHR) that explains complex healthcare systems and makes leading change easier. That effort led to this one: we approach the ICD-10 challenge in a similar fashion, with the new role of the provider in the coding process as the central issue. We conducted numerous focus groups with key decision-makers across a broad spectrum of providers that cemented our findings. Themes and patterns emerged around the impact of the provider's expertise and workflow as opposed to just the coder's. ICD-10 adoption demands that we reorient ourselves within a familiar environment and require a new level of responsibility from the traditional provider role.

This text provides a greater purpose beyond the adoption of a new coding system; it addresses the need to commit to something greater than a mandate. Healthcare leaders who fully understand the magnitude of change in documentation and coding will reap the benefits, and in the course of doing so, will build competencies in large-scale organizational change, a strategic differentiator in a rapidly evolving healthcare industry.

We believe that a strong point of view is needed to help advance the preparation of people and providers for the inevitable introduction of ICD-10. The following five assertions frame the text within this book:

1. **Don't wait: Prepare today.** Full clinical adoption must trump the risk abatement approach that comes with a typical mandate. In fact, providers must aggressively prepare for the changes in terms of the provider's new role. Those who take the opportunity to prepare today will be the lucky ones come October, 2013; the unlucky will be those who hoped the mandate would just go away.

2. **Positioning is critical.** Expect significant resistance to the idea that providers have a new level of responsibility for coding. ICD-9 is an outdated system. Leaders and providers who understand the value of improved clinical documentation will use the tool to their advantage.

3. **Appeal to the provider's intellect.** Critical thinking must outweigh emotion as we consider the change in the provider role. Prepare to fully examine this new system that demands we change our old methods of clinical documentation and workflow. Help providers accept the positive impact along

with the more granular level of responsibility by addressing the complexities of ICD-10 at a systematic level.

4. **Address fear head on.** Misinformation and propaganda about ICD-10 fuels the already reticent provider, allowing fear to overpower reason. A leadership plan to supply facts and data on the true impact to the provider will greatly reduce fear and support the process of change.

5. **Invest wisely and early in training and communication.** The provider must learn new coding requirements and understand the overall plan to adopt ICD-10. Size new skill requirements by role to demonstrate that learning a new workflow is not as daunting as providers might initially believe. Address the new training requirements with an emphasis on the ongoing obligation to achieve efficiency and effectiveness.

The objective of our research is to examine the barriers and opportunities of ICD-10 adoption with a special focus on the leaders of this effort and the providers' new role. We understand that this research is a continuous body of work and that the future will present additional challenges that we cannot see at this time. We also believe that we are participating in the transformation of healthcare through information technology, making these truly the best of times in healthcare.

●

A note on definitions: We recognize that the terms used for healthcare providers today can be ambiguous and that predefining our use in this text may be helpful. We use the term *provider* to describe anyone who provides care, including physicians, physician assistants, nurses, hospitals, physician practices, and so forth. We are careful to use the most specific term possible whenever appropriate.

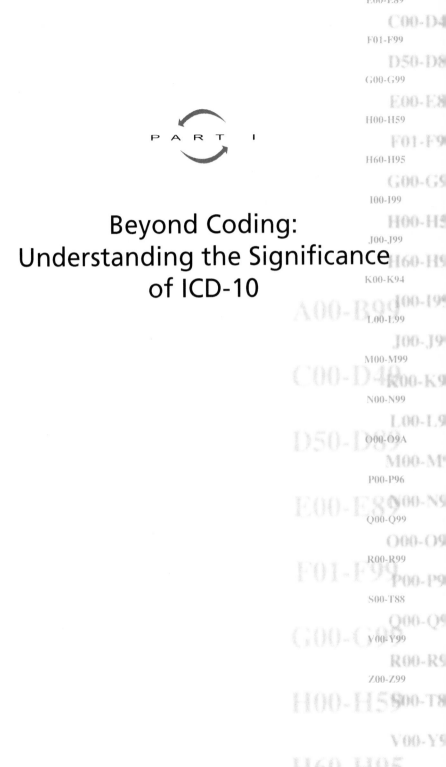

P A R T   I

Beyond Coding:
Understanding the Significance
of ICD-10

As if Electronic Medical Record (EMR) adoption, meaningful use attestation, Healthcare Reform, and the move toward Accountable Care Organizations (ACOs) aren't causing enough tension, healthcare leaders and providers now face the largest healthcare mandate in history. Completing the transition to the International Classification of Disease, 10th Edition, Clinical Modification/Procedure Coding System (ICD-10) is equivalent to mastering a new language. The magnitude of the change required is daunting. ICD-10 brings a complete shift in code structure and format, over 140,000 new codes, exponential specificity, and new transaction standards. For healthcare executives, it couldn't come at a more challenging time – while all are short on time and money.

In an attempt to understand how healthcare executives are preparing for the transition from ICD-9 to ICD-10, we conducted numerous focus groups with key decision-makers throughout the country. These conversations exposed the collective mindshare that this transition will significantly impact coders and IT applications. While we agree that coder training and application readiness are critical, they are only the tip of the ICD-10 iceberg. Consider what lies beneath: the need to document at a much higher level of specificity from the initial patient encounter, meaning that responsibility now falls to the provider instead of to the coder. We also discovered a profound lack of appreciation for the financial threat of noncompliance with ICD-10's high level of coding specificity. We must help providers master and document in this new language at this new level of specificity or face significant negative impact to the bottom line.

Our research shows that the transition to ICD-10 is an all-or-nothing proposition. Decision-makers must prioritize clinical documentation in the ICD-10 adoption strategy or put the organization at huge financial risk. Compliance with minimal requirements will damage a provider's financial health beyond repair, as resulting cash shortages will quickly outweigh any efforts at recovery after the fact. In Table 1, we contrast the differences between a singular focus on compliance and a strategy of accurate coding beginning with the provider. It is clear which one results in ICD-10 adoption and fundamentally benefits providers the most.

	Mandate	Adoption
Driver	Compliance with law	Opportunity to improve
Strategy	Survival	Improve Quality
Financial Focus	Avoid costs	Improve Accuracy of Charge Capture
Motivation	Avoid penalties	Pursue Improvements in Documentation, Coding Accuracy and Public Surveillance Reporting
Effort Level	Minimal	Provider and Leader Engagement
Emotion	Resentment/Fear	Assured/Confident
Performance Level	Behavior Monitoring Necessary	Metrics-Driven
Specificity	Minimal	Maximized
Transition Management	"It's just a project"	Fundamental organizational change

Table 1: Coding Mandate Vs. ICD-10 Adoption

Whether by simple compliance with the mandate or a true adoption approach, providers must fully transition to ICD-10 by October 1, 2014. Pursuing mere compliance, however, is a highly risky strategy given the threat of losses in revenue, productivity and market position, as well as the risk of financial disincentives for non-compliance.

We strongly believe that providers have every-

> **"We strongly believe that providers have everything to gain by taking the immediate opportunity to align ICD-10 adoption efforts with other current, valuable initiatives, such as EMR adoption."**

thing to gain by taking the immediate opportunity to align ICD-10 adoption efforts with other current, valuable initiatives, such as EMR adoption. EMR and ICD-10 adoption are both wide-reaching initiatives that affect many provider roles. Both demand changes in workflow, policies and procedures, and technology applications. Both support enhanced data capture, consistent with the objective of meaningful use. Both initiatives require a commitment to significant organizational change. A single approach that unites EMR and ICD-10 adoption initiatives maximizes value for the provider organization as it faces fundamental change. Considering the challenges of improving clinical documentation, aligning the efforts of the ICD-10 transition with EMR adoption is a winning strategy.

11

As we studied the challenges of ICD-10 adoption, we found that a successful transition to ICD-10 depends equally on the interaction of the same key components we identified in our previous research: engaged leadership, proficient providers, metrics and a plan for sustainment. Leaders who embrace these critical components give the organization an advantage in the ICD-10 adoption effort.

Why Now?

I t's 1977. Jimmy Carter succeeds Gerald Ford as the 39th President of the United States, the Oakland Raiders defeat the Minnesota Vikings in Super Bowl XI and Fleetwood Mac's Grammy-winning album *Rumours* is released. This year also introduced the first Commodore PET (Personal Electronic Transactor) and the founding of Apple Computer; the veritable beginning of the personal computer age as we know it. And, perhaps not as groovy as Steve Jobs' Apple Computer, the World Health Organization published The International Classification of Diseases, 9th Revision, Clinical Modification (ICD-9-CM), commonly referred to as ICD-9.

Consider for a moment the rapid and continuous advancement of medical care and technologies over the past 34 years - breathtaking! Now, ponder the effects of a coding system designed over three decades ago intersecting and integrating with today's technology - frightening! It is time to adopt a

> "ICD-10 codes represent significant advancements in medicine and technology over the past three decades."

coding system worthy of the 21st century. As adoption of EHRs accelerates, transfers of digital knowledge increase, and more diagnostic information is shared than ever before, we must have code sets that accommodate greater specificity, current terminology, and expanded concepts for injuries, laterality, and other important factors. ICD-10 codes represent significant advancements in medicine and technology over the past three decades. It is time to give 1977 its coding system back and to move toward a system that is current, accurate, and accommodating of medicines' innovative nature.

As healthcare leaders, we already feel like we are swimming in priorities, but the ICD-10 mandate looms. Implicating virtually every entity and role found in our healthcare system today, ICD-10 permeates every interaction between them. The challenge of changing old behaviors to adopt ICD-10 is formidable. Costs are short-term, benefits long-term. Basic compliance is the minimum required by law as of October 1, 2014. Providers who simply comply with the basic mandate, investing only in infrastructure to fulfill the government mandate, may

13

"The challenge of changing old behaviors to adopt ICD-10 is formidable. Costs are short-term, benefits long-term."

survive for the short term, only to be surpassed by providers with cash and more effective growth plans. Organizations in this scenario risk serious negative financial impact. On the opposite end of the spectrum are leaders taking the opportunity to drive strategic growth by using ICD-10 to capitalize on advanced clinical capabilities not offered by providers lagging behind in the ICD-10 transition. Advanced clinical capabilities are enabled not only by ICD-10 but also by other complementary codes sets such as the Systematized Nomenclature of Medicine – Clinical Terms (SNOMED). The goal is to achieve a robust set of clinical terms that support more effective communication and analysis of clinical procedures and outcomes. To be a top competitor in the market, healthcare leaders must commit to a new level of provider documentation over mere compliance with the new rule. As summarized in Table 1, a provider's choice between complying with a mandate or adopting the new coding system is a critical decision that determines the level of engagement and the value received from ICD-10.

> "To be a top competitor in the market, healthcare leaders must commit to a new level of provider documentation over mere compliance with the new rule."

Why introduce this significant effort now? ICD-10 comes on the heels of a host of government mandates and healthcare IT priorities, including the prerequisite transition to version 5010 standards for HIPAA electronic health transactions. The new coding system is an integral part of the EHR's promise of cost reduction and quality improvement. ICD-9 has run out of capacity and cannot support developments in medical technology, diagnoses, or procedures. The United States is the only industrialized nation that has not adopted ICD-10 and we have managed to avoid it for 30 years. If now is not the time, then when? If we push the date further back, we only delay the inevitable. The time is now to make ICD-10 an integral part of EMR adoption.

> **"The time is now to make ICD-10 an integral part of EMR adoption."**

15

• • • The Greater Purpose • • •

The healthcare industry cannot afford to ignore advanced technologies that enable sharing of information. There is a greater purpose here. Consider Francis Bacon, the seventeenth century proponent of the scientific revolution, who viewed science and technology as existing to improve the human condition. As Bacon put it, the "true and lawful end of the sciences is that human life be enriched by new discoveries and powers." Four centuries later, Einstein echoed Bacon in a speech at Cal Tech: "Concern for man himself and his fate must form the chief interest of all technical endeavors."

We cannot ignore the prevalence of technology and its ability to enrich our existence, especially in healthcare. To continue improving the human condition through science and technology – specifically healthcare technology – we must consider the interaction of technology, providers and patients, and the data we gather to improve care. ICD-10 provides a framework of over 140,000 different codes that permit myriad new discoveries and diagnoses to be tracked. Sharing this information on a global scale is an effort worth our time and attention; it is an endeavor consistent with Bacon and Einstein's vision to improve the human condition.

However, the introduction of the expanded coding system and the herculean effort to implement the required new technologies and documentation come at a difficult time. The federal mandate and deadline create an unnatural crisis for healthcare providers already stressed by the introduction of EHRs and other new technologies.

> **"Healthcare entities stand to gain in varying ways, with patients and the general public being the largest beneficiaries."**

The benefits of ICD-10 adoption are associated with improvements in two areas: healthcare quality and healthcare cost reimbursements. As illustrated in Table 2, healthcare entities stand to gain in varying ways, with patients and the general public being the largest beneficiaries. Increased worldwide use of the ICD-10 standard, with its greater level of data specificity, enables improvements in public healthcare, particularly in areas such as comparison of morbidity and mortality data, and anticipation of demand for services. Public health surveillance, or tracking the occurrence and spread of disease and outcomes of treatment decisions, improves significantly, benefiting medical researchers and government and non-profit healthcare agencies. In the area of healthcare cost reimbursements, primary benefits include support for fraud identification, increased accuracy of claims processing (including substantiation of medical necessity), and the ability to measure healthcare services quality, en-

17

abling value-based purchasing and pay-for-performance methodologies.

While ICD-10 adoption impacts public healthcare worldwide, many providers grapple with how it directly affects their individual situations. Healthcare leaders struggling to comply may fail to recognize the benefits of improving documentation and coding processes. Providers benefit from greater specificity in patient-specific clinical decision support and the improvement in quality of care. They also benefit from the identification of best practices, as do all healthcare entities. And, while healthcare cost reimbursement benefits primarily payers, providers share in the benefit of improved claims processing accuracy, particularly when it results in fewer code interpretation differences, more timely reimbursement, and revenue gains from a more comprehensive list of reimbursed procedures. Depending on the structure of performance incentives, providers may also benefit from improved measurement of healthcare services quality. Although complicated by misaligned incentives for the various stakeholders, the fact remains that commitment to ICD-10 offers valuable opportunities and embodies a purpose much greater than a government mandate.

> **"Healthcare leaders struggling to comply may fail to recognize the benefits of improving documentation and coding processes."**

Benefit	Providers	Health Information Management	Healthcare Leaders	Payers	Patients and the Public
Public health surveillance	X				X
Comparison of morbidity and mortality data	X				X
Patient-specific clinical decision support	X				X
Medical Research	X				X
Identification of best practices	X	X	X	X	X
Accuracy of claims processing*	X +/–	X	X	X	X +/–
Fraud Identification				X	X
Ability to measure enabling pay for performance	X +/–		X	X	X
Ability to measure healthcare services quality	X		X	X	X
Increased specificity for describing clinical care	X	X	X	X	X

Table 2: ICD-10 Benefits Matrix

*It remains to be seen if ICD-10-based claims will result in aggregate changes to payment levels for providers, and for patients. A 3M Health Information Systems study of the anticipated effects on hospital payments conclude that, best case, hospitals will experience a change in payment levels ranging from a negligible (.05%) increase to a modest (0.38%) decrease, depending on the methodologies payers use. (3M Health Information Systems)

- Come to terms quickly with expanding the provider's role in better, more specific documentation.

- Aggressively pursue quality care improvement through enhanced documentation and reporting methods.

- Act now. The time is now to make ICD-10 an integral part of EMR adoption. We must overcome our history of delay and failure and succeed at this transition.

- Go big or go home! The greater purpose is more compelling than a mandate. Consider the intersection of efforts to adopt both an EMR and ICD-10 to create value for all stakeholders. Healthcare leaders, providers, coders, and patients all benefit from improved clinical decision support and reporting on healthcare services quality.

P A R T   I I

Providers Move to Center Stage

A Google search on the term "ICD-10 consultant" yields over a million results, showing that the growth of ICD-10 consulting services is in response to a real need. It is clear that healthcare leaders are asking for help. In our focus group research, nearly 90% of healthcare leaders reported using an outside consultant to perform an ICD-10 assessment. As we delved deeper in these discussions, most providers asked for help in two areas: coder education and training, and IT assessments, upgrades and testing. Shockingly, fewer than 5% mentioned improved clinical documentation as a priority in their ICD-10 strategy. The change is seismic, considering the underlying economic and social impact of Version 10. We are at risk of the coder fulfilling the central role as agent, arbiter and mediator instead of the provider. If we do not fully define the role of the provider in ICD-10 and connect providers

> "If we do not fully define the role of the provider in ICD-10 and connect providers to a new business model, the move to a new coding system will have been an enormous investment for little or no clinical value."

22

to a new business model, the move to a new coding system will have been an enormous investment for little or no clinical value.

In 1904, the first known management consultant in the United States, Mary Parker Follet, invented what she called "The Law of the Situation." Her law required every business to occasionally ask itself the question: "What business am I really in?" For example, she convinced a small client of hers, a window shade manufacturer, that he was in the light control business rather than the window treatments business. The timely and realistic application of Follet's question helps redirect a myopic view on compliance and uncovers a provider's greater purpose – one that can rally the Chief Financial Officer as well as the provider. If Mary were here to help us today, no doubt she would ask us this important question: "In terms of ICD-10, what business are we really in?" Are we in the coding business? The answer to this question fundamentally changes the way we view our work and our common purpose.

Providers are passionate about and committed to the work of discovery, diagnosis, healing and learning, not coding. Yet ICD-10 is being sold as a coding mandate requiring absolute compliance. No wonder many see little value in it. What if instead, the ICD-10 transition were aligned with improving patient care? Consider the power and value of aligning a provider's passion for patient care with a specific way to improve the results of the work they love. Earlier, we discussed how ICD-10 can significantly improve how providers care for patients, including clinical decision support, increased specificity in describing clinical care and increased accuracy of public health surveillance. In the discussion that follows, we turn our attention to the importance of healthcare leaders understanding what business they are in, in terms of ICD-10 – the business of improving the quality and accuracy of healthcare reporting data, with the goal of improved public health surveillance, the reduction of healthcare costs, and improved clinical care.

"Consider the power and value of aligning a provider's passion for patient care with a specific way to improve the results of the work they love."

New Roles for Physicians, Healthcare Leaders and Coders

Every June, we gather 100 of the most influential healthcare leaders together to ponder, debate and innovate around the most challenging issues facing us in healthcare IT. The Healthcare Forum never disappoints in uncovering critical issues and inspiring new thinking. These discussions directly influence the direction of our subsequent research and publications. At a recent Healthcare Forum, a group of healthcare leaders that included a CEO, several CIOs, and a CFO were enjoying lunch, when the discussion moved to ICD-10. The tone of the conversation and comments caught our attention. Several shared the current state of ICD-10 transition work they were experiencing; they focused on updating systems, testing applications, discussing updates with vendors, and worrying about coder readiness. In the conversation, we heard not one mention of the vital provider role in the transition.

Among executive leaders, clinical documentation does not seem to be a priority in planning for this monumental transition. In our focus group discussions, over 75% of healthcare IT leaders viewed ICD-10 as a mandate out of their control. In contrast, only 25% of healthcare IT leaders were prepared to use the ICD-10 transition as an opportunity to improve clinical documentation, clinical decision support, and overall quality reporting. Most healthcare leaders recognize the importance of updating systems to comply with HIPAA 5010, and also the need to educate coders, but very few are prepared for the enormous effort of changing how physicians document care. Considering the potential financial risk for providers, the transition to ICD-10 deserves a

"The transition to ICD-10 has the potential to put healthcare providers out of business."

lot more attention from C-level executives. Imagine how the delays from inadequate specificity and inaccurate codes will impact cash flow. The transition to ICD-10 has the potential to put healthcare providers out of business. To understand and act upon the potential value of investing in this transition, leadership teams must engage immediately.

Role definition is paramount in navigating this transition. Refer to Table 3 to understand the contrast between key stakeholder roles in ICD-9 versus ICD-10 environments. We know that most providers will comply with HIPAA 5010 by January 1, 2012; therefore, we focus here on how documentation and coding processes need to change over the long term. Healthcare leaders must reprioritize the ICD-10 transition for the organization. Instead of watching from the sidelines while physicians and coders struggle to adjust to new roles, executive leaders must fully engage in the transition. Fully engaged leaders can in turn effectively communicate the clinical value of ICD-10 to department and physician leaders. We must also influence other entities in the healthcare system, such as payers, government agencies and vendors, whose actions and readiness will enable a successful transition.

> **"Physicians must fully commit to increasing specificity in their documentation efforts."**

Physicians must fully commit to increasing specificity in their documentation efforts. Gone are the days of relying on coders to interpret and extrapolate from incomplete notes. Coder retraining for ICD-10 requires more medical knowledge, far beyond learning new codes. Grasping the delta between ICD-9 and ICD-10 necessitates planning that addresses the barriers to a successful transition. Each stakeholder must prepare for a new role.

27

Stakeholder	ICD-9	ICD-10
Healthcare executives: **CEO, CIO, CFO, CMO, CMIO, CNO**	• Awareness that billing and coding processes exist	• Become informed about changes required for successful ICD-10 adoption • Prioritize ICD-10 transition • Communicate the clinical value to leaders • Influence external stakeholders
Providers	• Document care • Assign commonly used codes (physician offices)	• Commit to increased specificity in clinical documentation. • Accept responsibility for front-end coding process
Coders	• Assignment of ICD-9 codes • Extrapolation from various levels of documentation	• Learn advanced anatomy and physiology • Learn new coding structure • Commit to accuracy of code assignment

28

Table 3: Key Stakeholders

ICD-10 is quickly gaining attention among healthcare executives. To lead this effort, we must first assess the business impact of ICD-10 on the provider. A comprehensive review of the areas affected by ICD-10 is sobering. In our experience, healthcare executives underestimate the impact by threefold prior to assessment. ICD-10 impacts many more applications, roles, and processes than we initially expect.

> **"One of the most critical responsibilities of healthcare leaders is to create common purpose among department leaders and physician leaders who are expected to change the way they practice medicine."**

Healthcare leaders must engage, assess the impact and prioritize the effort. Simply heaping this mandate onto a long list of initiatives won't work. By prioritizing the effort and identifying synergies with other initiatives, leaders can serve the needs of the clinical staff. One of the most critical responsibilities of healthcare leaders is to create common purpose among department leaders and

> **"Healthcare leaders who strategically align the ICD-10 work with EMR adoption earn more physician support and ultimately best serve the needs of the business and the patients."**

physician leaders who are expected to change the way they practice medicine. Leaders must also influence external stakeholders, especially vendors and payers, to ease the burden on employees.

Garnering physician engagement will be one of the most challenging aspects of this conversion. To quote a physician from our recent Healthcare Forum debates, "I am not a coder. I don't expect ICD-10 to have a big impact on me." Forcing physicians to learn codes or invest time in a coding mandate will fall on deaf ears. Healthcare leaders who strategically align the ICD-10 work with EMR adoption earn more physician support and ultimately best serve the needs of the business and the patients. For physicians, true adoption of the new standards requires a different process for care documentation and calls for a major shift in responsibility for coding accuracy. By virtue of the authority they command and an upstream position in the diagnosis-to-coding lifecycle, physician leadership is critical. Identifying a compelling reason to improve clinical documentation is of the utmost importance – we all know that a government mandate isn't compelling enough on its own!

Strictly speaking, coders are responsible for accurately and completely translating the information into a standardized coding format. The focus on coder training and education is warranted considering the chasm between the ICD-9 coding world and the new world of ICD-10. Yet the accuracy of coder work is highly dependent on physicians who are responsible for the specificity of the diagnostic and procedural specifics. Without the specificity, coders' hands are tied. Even the most knowledgeable and proficient coders can't overcome lack of documentation.

Understanding and communicating the changes in role definition for the three key stakeholders, physicians, healthcare leaders and coders, is the first step in a successful transition to ICD-10.

The second step to better understanding ICD-10's inherent complexities is to look at the effort as a system of interrelated actions which result from providers' and coders' new roles. Without a method to describe the required changes, the move toward ICD-10 is sure to follow other failed change efforts. To tell this story, we once again call upon researchers at MIT and specifically the work of Professors Forrester and Senge.

Jay W. Forrester's biography tells the story of an electrical engineer who pioneered work in feedback control mechanisms for military equipment. In fact, he created one of the first aircraft flight simulators for the U.S. Navy, which led to the earliest computerized combat information systems. He is known for his many inventions and patents in computer technology, including technology that facilitated the digital control of machines. Yet one of his most noteworthy accomplishments came as a result of his appreciation for the complexity of organizational change. "Forrester's experiences as a manager led him to conclude that the biggest impediment to progress comes not from the engineering side of industrial problems, but from the management side." In a surprising career shift, Jay Forrester became a professor at Massachusetts Institute of Technology's Sloan School of Management, and went on to do some of his most innovative work there. Today he is recognized as the creator of "system dynamics," a field popularized by Peter Senge that is often referred to as *systems thinking* (U.S. Department of Energy, 1997).

Early in our research of clinical documentation, we knew that we would need a systemic view of change in order to get both leaders and providers involved. The systems thinking approach is fundamentally different from that of traditional forms of analysis and is a great fit for the healthcare pragmatist. Traditional analysis of complex issues separates and analyzes individual aspects of the system. In contrast, systems thinking focuses on the interactions between constituents of the system and the interdependencies between our actions and those taken by others. Expanding our view to include the interactions within the system results in strikingly different conclusions compared to traditional forms of analysis, especially in complex healthcare systems that drive both clinical and financial outcomes.

> **"The systems thinking approach is fundamentally different from that of traditional forms of analysis and is a great fit for the healthcare pragmatist."**

To put the complex system in a format to tell its story, we use feedback loops, the primary tool used in systems thinking. We will use this format throughout the remainder of this book. Feedback processes are actions that reinforce or counteract (balance) each other. These processes are at play in all systems that require human decisions or actions. They can be diagrammed as causal loops so that the reader can see the story play out in the relationships between variables. A reinforcing feedback process results in either the acceleration or deceleration of growth. A balancing feedback process operates as a stabilizer, putting the brakes on both acceleration and deceleration, seeking a state of equilibrium (Senge, 1994).

In Figures 1 and 2, we use the cause-and-effect relationship between exercise, health and energy to provide examples of reinforcing feedback processes. Figure 1 is a simple loop depicting positive reinforcement. This diagram shows how participation in an exercise program results in improved mental and physical health that in turn drives increased energy, reinforcing continued participation in the exercise program. In contrast, the loop in Figure 2 tells a negative reinforcing story, where skipping workouts results in feeling less mentally and physically fit and less energetic, driving a continual decrease in exercise.

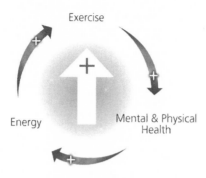

Figure 1: The Positive Reinforcing Process of Exercise

Note: In these figures, and throughout the remainder of this book, we use the convention of an upward arrow with a plus sign to represent positive reinforcing action and a downward arrow with a minus sign to represent negative reinforcing action.

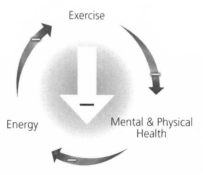

Figure 2: The Negative Reinforcing Process of Exercise

Continuing with the exercise example, Figure 3 depicts the balancing feedback process that exists between time spent exercising and time available to exercise. We continually juggle our goal of exercise with all of the other demands on our time. When a constraint such as lack of time interferes with the exercise goal, a gap is created between the desired and actual frequency of exercise. Balancing processes underlie all goal-oriented behavior, but they can be difficult to recognize, especially in more complex processes (Senge, 1994). When balancing processes go unnoticed, we tend to apply solutions before fully understanding the problem.

In the exercise example, we need to free up time by modifying or dropping other activities to lessen or remove the constraint, leading to more workouts and a reduction in the gap between desired and actual results. The scale symbol is the convention we use to indicate a balancing feedback process.

35

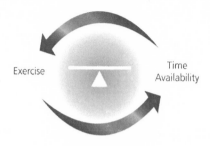

Figure 3: A Balancing Feedback Process: The Relationship Between Time and Exercise

No presentation of systems thinking fundamentals is complete without mention of delays. Recognizing and understanding the influence of delays in complex processes is one of the most valuable tools in decision-making and will greatly assist our full comprehension of the changes on the way. Delays, or interruptions between actions and their consequences, permeate both reinforcing and balancing feedback processes. In the exercise example, if we do not measure the desired frequency against the actual frequency of exercise, we may not realize whether we are in a positive or negative reinforcing cycle. In addition, we may not see the benefits of exercise immediately, making the relationship between the exercise and improved well-being less obvious. As a result, we might give up too soon on the exercise program - or overshoot and increase exercise activity in a way that causes injury. Likewise, efforts to address constraints take time to work, especially given the more complex processes found on the financial side of healthcare. The ability to recognize and overcome the effects created by delays is critical to establishing the patience needed while waiting for expected outcomes. Often, a well-developed system diagram exposes a time variable, such as a lack thereof or delay in, as the critical variable within the system.

37

Given a basic understanding of systems thinking and the use of feedback loops as a storytelling device, we can now develop a narrative around the inevitable changes accompanying ICD-10. We strongly believe that the best, most sustainable way forward is to expose the barriers to adoption by dealing with them openly to remove them rather than forcing compliance by pushing a new system onto wary and skeptical providers.

To manage the barriers, we must understand and represent them as they exist in a system of reinforcing variables and actions. To do this, let's assume for a moment we can describe ICD-10 in a barrier-free environment. We know that the transition to ICD-10 demands a higher level of precision in patient diagnosis and treatment procedure documentation than the level necessitated by ICD-9. To transition to ICD-10, we must establish a reinforcing

> "We strongly believe that the best, most sustainable way forward is to expose the barriers to adoption by dealing with them openly to remove them rather than forcing compliance by pushing a new system onto wary and skeptical providers."

cycle of growth, as illustrated in the causal loop diagram in Figure 4. The reinforcing growth cycle begins with providers documenting at a high level of detail during initial clinical inquiry and observation, and continues with consistent and complete documentation of those findings. As the systematic story unfolds, precision in documentation at the initial point of contact results in an appropriately specific diagnosis, providing coders with what they need in order to code accurately and efficiently. Over time, standardized, accurate coding provides a basis for healthcare providers to compare disease and treatment outcomes, allowing them to reinforce patient-specific treatment and decision-making. The result is better quality healthcare that in turn helps providers reaffirm commitment to improved documentation. As shown in the inner cycle of Figure 4, improved specificity in clinical documentation also provides for accurate claims payment. Appropriately specific ICD-10 codes enable payers to determine coverage and cost categories accurately, which supports timely claims reimbursement, again reinforcing the provider's commitment to precise documentation.

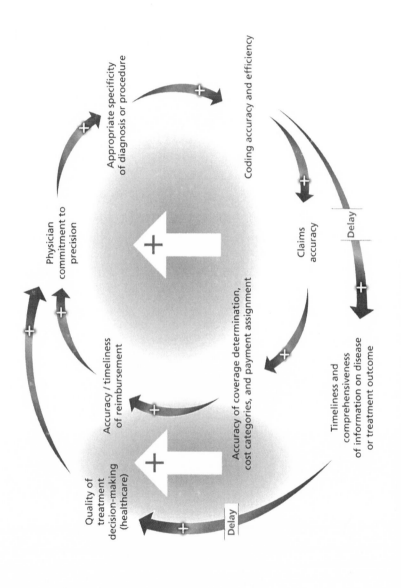

Figure 4: A Methodology for Healthcare Quality and Reimbursement Accuracy

Now that we have the story for a successful ICD-10 growth model, we can address the very real barriers that may keep us from adopting the new coding system. If enough detailed data is not captured in the initial encounter, then coding and claims accuracy is compromised. Aggregated data that might otherwise support clinical decision-making is also then unavailable. Claims processing is adversely impacted, resulting in reimbursement delays and cash flow interruptions. These experiences erode provider commitment and result in a negative reinforcing cycle that is difficult to reverse.

As noted, one of the most ubiquitous and crucial variables is the delay factor, or the distance in time between actions and their consequences. The longer the delay between an action and its positive consequence, the harder it is to sustain that action. In the ICD-10 transition, we understand that we are facing a psychological difficulty of working harder now in order to save time and see improvements in the future. We understand the logic of fundamental system change, but the lure of a quick fix threatens to derail our efforts.

The delays depicted in Figure 4 indicate that the benefits of better quality healthcare and timely reimbursement are not immediate. It is a lengthy process to take a single diagnosis, aggregate it with other data, analyze similarities and effects, and report findings. Indeed, it may take years before providers perceive that

41

treatment decision-making has benefited from greater coding specificity.

Delays characterize the reimbursement process as well, as seen in Figure 5. Even under ideal conditions, the diagnosis-to-code assignment process is also characterized by delays. Depending on the number of roles involved in coding, the processing time from diagnosis to code assignment varies widely. For a hospital that practices concurrent reviews performed by nurses and other clinical documentation improvement (CDI) personnel, and that employs professional coders, the time between provider diagnosis and code assignment can be accomplished in just a few hours. However, if documentation is insufficient, coders have to stop and query the provider for additional detail, creating unexpected delays. The longer the time lapse between initial diagnosis and coding attempt, the poorer the provider's recall of the diagnostic details may be. Time delay is compounded based on how far downstream the deficiency is identified. A process that should span a few hours can become rework that spans days.

"If documentation is insufficient, coders have to stop and query the provider for additional detail, creating unexpected delays."

42

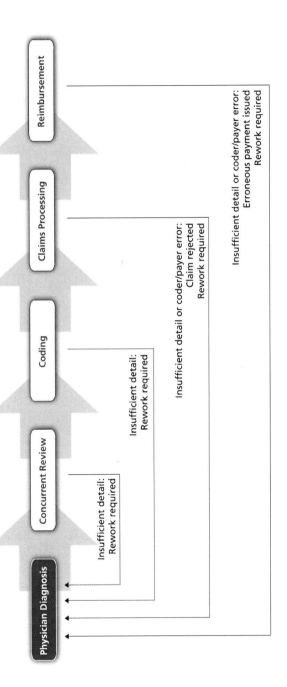

Figure 5: Delays and Rework Shown As a Linear Timeline

Rework often creates backlogs, generating more work for the same number of resources. Coders may be reluctant to query physicians, inadvertently sacrificing coding accuracy. Even when coders receive perfectly documented diagnoses or procedures, a number of factors can affect coding efficiency, introducing delay into the reimbursement process. In the initial stages of transition, the amount of time it takes experienced coders to translate provider notes into a standard code is expected to increase, due to the greater specificity of ICD-10 codes. In addition, coders must "unlearn" ICD-9 codes and grasp a new conceptual structure. For those providers unburdened by knowledge of ICD-9, evidence suggests that ICD-10 codes are in fact more logical and easier to understand.

Inaccurately coded claims may be rejected, requiring recoding and re-submittal. Alternatively, inaccurate claims may result in payment errors. Errors may consist of overpayment, risking subsequent payer recovery actions, or underpayment, resulting in revenue loss. Underpaid providers submit appeals, triggering rework to recover lost revenue. As seen in Figure 5, delays at each step in the process cause accurate reimbursement to be delayed, halted, or reversed as the process starts over at square one.

Providers are dependent on payers for the final stage of the healthcare services delivery process, where claims are processed and payments made. Payer and provider efficiencies are intertwined. Payer inability to accurately and efficiently apply

ICD-10 standards to determine coverage and assign payment significantly slows the reimbursement process, triggering the need for provider audits and subsequent appeals.

When healthcare leaders recognize the delay factor in its many forms – rework, productivity loss, backlogs, postponed realization of benefits – and understand its effects, they can better manage expectations and identify strategies that minimize delays. As we have noted, one potential delay inherent in a new coding system is a reimbursement delay. Understanding and managing the causes of delays like these can avert a financial mess.

ICD-10 adoption is subject to many of the same barriers associated with the adoption of an EMR: resistant providers, constrained resources, disengaged leadership, and a lack of measurement to assess both clinical and financial outcomes. In a complex system like healthcare, a multitude of interrelated factors drive behavior. Figure 6 summarizes a number of constraints likely to inhibit a positive reinforcing cycle of ICD-10 adoption from the perspective of timely reimbursement. Our focus is on the constraints that directly impact providers.

45

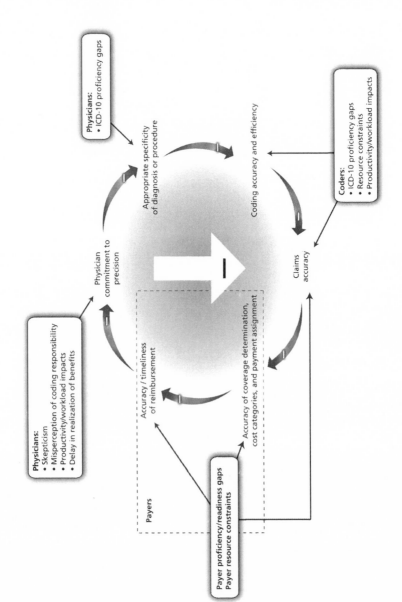

Figure 6: Barriers to ICD-10 Adoption

Consider that the bar-
riers identified in Figure 6
are additive to bad habits
carried over from ICD-9.
The limitations of ICD-9
lead to workarounds and
default behaviors that

> **"Lack of specificity in ICD-9 has contributed to a lack of perceived value in billing codes for clinical reporting, negatively impacting physician engagement."**

diminish the usefulness of billing codes for clinical reporting. For example, the use of the code "unspecified" is of
little clinical value and is commonly over-used today. Many
researchers have experienced disappointment in billing
data that inaccurately describes clinical care. Lack of specificity in ICD-9 has contributed to a lack of perceived value
in billing codes for clinical reporting, negatively impacting
physician engagement.

Even though we believe that physicians are not in the
coding business, we cannot ignore the cause and effect relationship between cod-
ing specificity and reim-
bursement. Physicians
who perceive that ICD-10
specificity serves billing
purposes instead of pa-

> **"We cannot ignore the cause and effect relationship be-tween coding specificity and reimbursement."**

tient care are apt to conclude that it is the payers who benefit and that both physicians and patients may be harmed financially. The physician-payer relationship is in many instances an uneasy one. Physicians have experienced inconsistencies and gaps in payer use of HIPAA standards to date, and perceive this behavior as having thwarted physician attainment of administrative efficiencies (American Medical Association (AMA), 2008). Resentment of payers makes physicians loath to use a new standard that may benefit the payers further at physician expense. Additionally, the relationship between physicians and coders is often a transactional one in which coders provide a distant service to physicians. Physicians often take the stance that diagnostic and procedural coding is a clerical task for which coders have primary responsibility.

> **"Resentment of payers makes physicians loath to use a new standard that may benefit the payers further at physician expense."**

As we heard in many of our interviews and focus groups, change is not free and is clearly not painless. Additional rigor required for documenting diagnoses and procedures translates into increased workload for physicians. This increase most likely will be permanent, but measures highest in the earliest transition stages. The Natchimson study reports an anticipated increase in documentation activities for ICD-10-CM that will result in an expected increase of 3-4% in physician time spent on documentation (Natchimson Advi-

48

sors LLC, 2008). Demands on physicians relative to quality reporting are also expected to increase with the move to ICD-10. Quality measures will likely undergo updating, requiring physicians to change reported data. In the interim, they may be called upon to translate

"As we heard in many of our interviews and focus groups, change is not free and is clearly not painless."

ICD-9 codes to ICD-10 for measures in the Physician Quality Reporting Initiative (PQRI) (AMA, 2008).

Beyond the barriers for physicians, coder education and productivity are very prominent constraints. Ensuring coders are proficient will require a long-term investment in *continual* education for coders. Give coders the opportunity to work with the ICD-10 codes and to accumulate experience with complex clinical scenarios; proficiency will directly impact productivity. The more experience gained using the ICD-10 codes, the better prepared they will be to handle increased workloads. The literature suggests a potential productivity decrease of 50% for up to 4 - 6 months (Monegain, 2010; Morsch et al, 2010; Mair, 1999). Providers may be able to overcome some of those losses by working with physicians and coders early to prepare for the October 1, 2014 "Go Live". Because payers and vendors are also racing to prepare for ICD-10, resource constraints could influence efforts to adopt ICD-10. If providers and leaders experience delays in payment and slower

49

reimbursement early on, the perception of ICD-10 will suffer further.

Many of the barriers inhibiting physician engagement are the direct result of viewing the ICD-10 transition as a coding effort. The motivation for improving specificity in documentation should be tied to the providers' effort to adopt an EMR and to improve clinical outcomes. Those who have made significant progress in this area are already working hard to improve clinical documentation because it serves critical functionality in the EMR, like clinical decision support and quality reporting.

The ICD-10 reinforcing cycle (Figure 4) should be used to identify the stakeholders and critical components of a successful transition – one that focuses on healthcare quality and accurate reimbursement. Figures 5 and 6 identify the delays and the barriers that impact successful adoption of the new coding system. In Part III, we will use our understanding of systems thinking to discuss a sustainable process for achieving ICD-10 adoption.

• Redefine physician, healthcare leader and coder roles to align with ICD-10 compliance and EMR adoption.

• Recognize and communicate the significant expansion in responsibility for stakeholders in ICD-10 compared to ICD-9.

• Become conversant in systems thinking. Use the approach to inform shared understanding of the goal and its barriers and delays.

• Seek to understand the complexity of the ICD-10 reinforcing cycle and the interactions among physicians and coders.

• Identify all delays and obstacles; be brutally honest in this process.

• Prepare to handle the barriers most likely to inhibit ICD-10 adoption.

52

Developing a Plan that Fosters Trust

The previous section of this book depicts the complex story of ICD-10. In this tale we see the significant barriers, both overt and hidden, that challenge our best efforts to overcome them. We dedicate the remainder of this book to envisioning a way forward via a methodology supported by our experience with successful EMR adoption.

Start With the Brutal Facts

Jim Collins, author of *Good to Great* and widely-respected authority on effective leadership, speaks of the need for leaders to confront the brutal facts in order to positively influence change. Considering the leadership challenges facing those chosen to lead the ICD-10 charge, Jim's advice can direct us as we plan to adopt ICD-10. What are the two brutal facts overshadowing the other barriers mentioned previously?

First, there is distrust in government and new healthcare mandates. Since 1979, the Gallup Organization has polled Americans about trust in government and media. Today, distrust in government is near an all-time high, and for the fourth straight year, the majority of Americans say they have little or no trust in the mass media to report the news fully, accurately and fairly. Considering that healthcare is the second fastest-growing sector of the U.S. economy, employing over 12 million workers, skepticism is a sure bet among those facing another mandate with a looming deadline. For leaders and decision-makers facing this situation, the challenge seems insurmountable. For example, how can a leader help an employee begin to support a Congress distrusted for years? Many assume that all new coding requirements mandated from inside "The Beltway" are rife with cost and waste.

In a recent interview with Bill Spooner, the experienced CIO of Sharp HealthCare, he offered sage counsel for a leader seeking a way to overcome this brutal fact:

The focus is not on attempting to get your team to somehow trust the government. In fact, any attempt to do so will create an immediate repulse. Instead, direct your effort toward building trust between you and your team, and among your team. Be direct about the purpose of the change and be honest about the situation. These are very bright people; get them behind the greater purpose and the need for their involvement. Don't, however, expect them to alter their views on something you can't change.

The second barrier is fear. Fear of the unknown, of more work, of less time, of less income, of role changes...and fear of anything government-mandated. Fear is an emotion we all possess. It is infectious, especially when fueled by a collection of peers working under an ominous deadline and in the face of scarce available facts.

Take for example the stance by the AMA's House of Delegates on November 15th, 2011. They voted to "work vigorously to stop" the implementation of the ICD-10 diagnostic code set scheduled for October 1, 2014, and issued this statement: "The implementation of ICD-10 will create significant burdens on the practice of medicine with no direct benefit to individual patients' care," said Peter W. Carmel, MD, AMA president. "At a time when we are working to get the best value possible for our healthcare dollar, this massive and expensive undertaking will add administrative expense and create unnecessary workflow disruptions." Because the AMA is widely respected, this position should be taken seriously. Interestingly, The American Health Information Management Association (AHIMA) expressed an opposing view. Sue Bowman, Director of Coding Policy and Compliance, said: "AHIMA has demonstrated several times that administrative systems can be easily implemented for most primary practices, and that specialty practices will only be using a small number of the new codes." She also stated: "If the ICD-10 system had been implemented in the late 1990s, the problems created by constant delay would not be experienced today. She said "the U.S. system has essentially run out of codes and cannot accurately express current medical knowledge with the ICD-9 system."

The brutal facts we face in our efforts to conquer ICD-10 are ubiquitous distrust and fear. However, we know that addressing them up front increases the chances of successful adoption exponentially. The human brain is wired in such a way that our fear circuitry is more powerful than our reasoning faculties. Deep in the human brain is an area called the amygdala, a bundle of neurons that process the fear response. This area of the brain is capable of overwhelming the area that controls our consciousness, reason and rational thinking. We have an immutable self-preservation response in the face of danger, even when we are aware and try to stop it. To put it simply, the brain flinches first and asks questions later – sometimes much later.

As a result of our past research, we understand that the key components of health information technology adoption are engaged leadership, proficient providers, performance metrics, and sustainment. The same components are critical for ICD-10 adoption. Provider engagement is the critical initial step in achieving adoption, and its importance is influenced by two significant success-limiting factors: distrust and fear. First and foremost, leaders must overcome the distrust and fear surrounding the ICD-10 transition. Figure 7 shows how trust and confidence influence provider engagement. Leaders who create trust and overcome fear can engage others in the plan for adoption. Engaged providers are open to improving their understanding of the challenges they face. They are aware of the impact ICD-10 will have on their role and they appreciate the potential financial implications. They tackle issues head-on and align those efforts with the effort to improve critical care in ways that further boost engagement, progress and confidence.

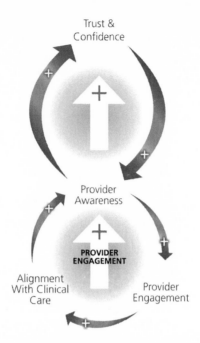

Figure 7: The Influence of Trust and Confidence on Leadership Engagement

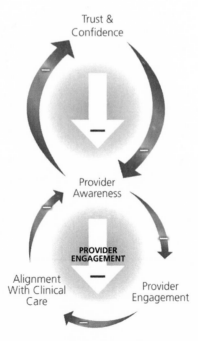

Figure 8: Lack of Trust and Confidence Leads to Minimal Provider Engagement

Leaders who ignore these brutal facts will find efforts to lead an adoption process constantly derailed by emotional tension in every aspect of the transition. Distrust and fear enable resistance. As resistance festers, providers disengage and organizational paralysis sets in. Adoption efforts falter. As shown in Figure 8, when trust and confidence wane, the wheel of progress becomes a cycle of decline. The adoption of ICD-10 depends on garnering trust and dispelling fear. This is a herculean effort, but it is manageable when we create a plan the team can be confident in.

60

Leadership: Create Engagement and Common Purpose

Even the most engaged, informed providers will likely find ICD-10 adoption efforts threatened by resistance from others. The formula for overcoming that resistance begins with a unified vision. Informed providers must articulate the impact of ICD-10 and proactively work to align the effort with EMR adoption, clinical documentation improvement, quality reporting initiatives, and coding productivity and accuracy. Once we garner trust and overcome fear, healthcare leaders and providers can execute a robust plan to prepare stakeholders for the coming dramatic changes. A solid plan will address each of three particular areas of challenge:

- **Leadership**: Become an informed leader. Communicate the value proposition for clinical care to foster provider engagement. Prioritize clinical documentation in the ICD-10 transition plan.

- **Education**: Enable providers to practice documenting with the ICD-10 required specificity. Initiate improved clinical documentation long before the deadline.

- **Metrics and Sustainment**: Develop a process for continually improving clinical documentation. Utilize documentation sampling to determine effectiveness.

Collect metrics focused on coding and documentation outcomes. Gauge the clinical and financial outcomes. Measure, improve, and measure again!

> **"Measure, improve, and measure again!"**

The amount of change and the pace of change in healthcare today are daunting to us all. Can we predict who will succeed in these uncertain times? For the transition to ICD-10, our research suggests that the core component and number one predictor of success is engagement. Healthcare and provider leaders must begin this quest by becoming better informed and more knowledgeable. A carefully orchestrated communication strategy results in trust, buy-in and acceptance of change, and begins by involving leaders from all areas of the organization. As we saw in Figure 7, trust and confidence reinforce provider engagement. As providers become better informed of their role and the potential impact of ICD-10, they become more engaged. Engaged providers work to help the organization align the adoption effort with improving clinical care, which in turn leads to the expansion and deepening of provider awareness and engagement.

> **"The core component and number one predictor of success is engagement."**

An important step is to develop a steering committee that includes leaders from senior management, finance, information technology, medical staff and health information management. These leaders are responsible for charting the course of ICD-10 adoption. Leaders should be authorized to allocate resources and identify high-level tasks and timelines. These leaders must be the voice of ICD-10 adoption for the rest of the staff.

Leaders set the tone and ensure communication flows through the organization and to appropriate external stakeholders. Not surprisingly, the rush to meet ICD-10 requirements prior to the October 1, 2014 Go Live puts a great deal of stress on vendors and payers as well as on internal stakeholders. The full adoption of ICD-10 requires business associates, including application vendors, payers and providers, to be ready. If vendors do not complete system upgrades in time, adoption efforts will be compromised. Given that system upgrades tend to be a significant effort, it is essential to get vendor commitment to the provider's timeline.

Make a comprehensive plan to overcome resistance in all its forms:

- If resistance to change is the common denominator in the organization, involve a few naysayers in the transition work. Imagine the value of a physician-led effort to assess the current state of clinical documentation and design the plan for improvement!
- Use real examples to demonstrate how improved data capture leads to better patient care. For finance-type stakeholders, show specific examples where compre-

hensive clinical documentation has made a huge positive impact on reimbursements.

- Hold open dialogues between leaders, providers and staff to counteract resentment. Discuss how leadership can influence both internal and external demands. For example, advocate that the Department of Health and Human Services (HHS) monitor and enforce payer compliance (AMA, 2008).

- Use patient record sampling to provide data showing how well current documentation supports the ability to code to the most detailed level possible in the ICD-10 code set (AMA, 2008). If current documentation already provides a high level of detail, this feedback will reinforce provider engagement and acceptance.

- Create opportunities for providers to interact with clinical documentation specialists. Providers are more likely to consider feedback from knowledgeable experts who also understand provider workflow. Help providers understand that their actions have far-reaching effects. Providers and coders alike are best served by viewing their association as a partnership in which each party contributes to the achievement of a common goal (Chavis, 2011).

"Providers and coders alike are best served by viewing their association as a partnership in which each party contributes to the achievement of a common goal."

- Consider IT solutions that make it easier to capture required specificity, especially solutions that cater to providers' preferred methods for documenting (Schwend, 2011).

- Be attentive to indirect influences on provider workload emanating from other sectors (coders, payers) and seek ways to mitigate negative effects.

- In planning, do not lose sight of the fact that there is limited time to react. Although we have over a year before October 1, 2014, not all of that time is available for preparation. All components of the transition must be ready in time to perform significant testing and remediation of issues before Go Live.

65

• • • Education: Develop Proficiency • • •
and Reinforce New Behaviors

I n 2007, we had the pleasure of working with a world-re-
nowned hospital on the West Coast. A pioneer in medical
advances and home to one of the most respected training
grounds for medical students, this hospital provides exceptional care. We helped more than 800 providers adopt a new
Radiology Information System (RIS) to replace their legacy
system. By employing metrics collection as part of our initial needs assessment, we were able to highlight organizational challenges otherwise difficult to identify. We began
by asking users to rate their knowledge of and confidence in
the legacy system. We specifically wanted to know if they felt
confidence in their ability to do their job in that system. In
spite of having been in use for 12 years, we found extremely
low adoption rates. Only 45% of users reported a high level
of knowledge in tasks specific to their job role, and less than
50% reported a high level of confidence in use of the system.
These low rates of adoption could be explained by several
things. Changes in workflow, staff turnover, and system
upgrades typically erode initial levels of adoption. Providers must commit to a relentless effort of continued education over time or they risk experiencing gaps in adoption

behavior that get wider with each passing week or month. Eroding adoption rates are not uncommon, even in high-performance organizations. Ensuring continued user proficiency is a huge effort, requiring ongoing attention.

> **"Eroding adoption rates are not uncommon, even in high-performance organizations."**

The second predictor of success in the transition to ICD-10 is proficiency levels of providers and coders. Compliance with the ICD-10 mandate is not possible without a significant change in both quantity and quality of clinical documentation – and the roles with the highest impact belong to providers and coders. Initial documentation will set direction for every code submitted to a payer, so provider proficiency at the diagnosis stage is mandatory and is where we focus our methodology. Figure 9 illustrates how engaged providers support specificity in documentation, leading them to proficiency in the knowledge required to document at the required level of specificity, further reinforcing their engagement.

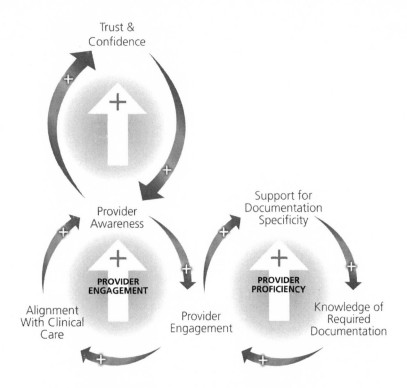

Trust &
Confidence

Provider
Awareness

**PROVIDER
ENGAGEMENT**

Alignment
With Clinical
Care

Provider
Engagement

Support for
Documentation
Specificity

**PROVIDER
PROFICIENCY**

Knowledge of
Required
Documentation

Figure 9: The Influence of Proficiency on Provider Engagement

Carefully consider the best strategies for developing and deploying education. Traditional methods such as train-the-trainer and classroom instruction are rarely effective in helping individuals acquire and apply knowledge. Born in 1850, Hermann Ebbinghaus is credited with uncovering one of the most depressing facts in all of education: people typically forget 90 percent of what they learn in a classroom within

> **"The most effective learning is designed to ensure proficiency by role."**

30 days (Medina, 2008). Poor learning experiences also result from variations in instructor style, overloading learners with too much information, and lack of specific instruction by role. The most effective learning is designed to ensure proficiency by role. Clinical documentation improvement education needs to ensure that providers achieve knowledge and confidence in documentation methods that support the new coding system.

A well-designed curriculum begins with mapping the value proposition of ICD-10 with the provider role. For example, ICD-10 code specificity will improve public health surveillance reporting, but only if providers document care at the highest level of specificity. Identifying the value proposition in each area will help identify the threshold proficiency by role. *Threshold proficiency* signifies the exact moment when a user has gained adequate knowledge to deliver on the value proposition.

"By definition, threshold proficiency aligns the user with the provider's vision and performance strategy, and signifies the moment at which knowledge links to quality of care."

By definition, threshold proficiency aligns the user with the provider's vision and performance strategy, and signifies the moment at which knowledge links to quality of care (Fred, 2002).

Provider proficiency in clinical documentation is fundamental to adoption. The more providers perceive the new conceptual framework and level of detail as aligned with their natural cognitive process, the greater the willingness to adopt a new level of specificity in diagnoses and treatment plans. Patient interactions begin with initial inquiry and observation by the physician, who must observe with an eye to ICD-10-appropriate specificity in order to document correctly.

Implications for proficiency development in providers:
- Encourage interaction between coders and physicians. Foster a new working relationship between these two critical stakeholders.
- Share the explicit nature of ICD-10's conceptual structure; encourage providers to draw parallels to their individual cognitive processes.
- Evaluate samples of a variety of medical records to determine to what extent existing documentation practices already support the level of detail needed for ICD-10.
- Consider changes to documentation capture processes to facilitate improvement. For example, add prompts to EMRs to remind providers to think about specificity from the start of an encounter (AHIMA, 2011).
- Create training on familiar platforms, using tools already supported by the provider. For example, simulate the incumbent EMR upgraded to ICD-10, or train within the framework of a superbill already in use.

- Designate a physician or provider champion who can emphasize quality of care initiatives as a method of promoting clinical documentation education.
- Publish findings from documentation reviews to emphasize the value of concise and high-quality data capture (AHIMA, 2011).
- Link provider training with coder training in a simulated flow of the communication required as diagnostic conclusions are transformed into coded representations.

• • • Metrics and Sustainment: Measure • • •
Outcomes and Sustain the Change

Approximately 50 million Americans go on diets every year. They drastically change the way they eat, commit to strenuous exercise programs, and deprive themselves of sweets, carbohydrates and anything else on the list of bad foods. Expecting the pounds to drop off quickly, they become frustrated when the weight comes off slowly and consistently – just like they gained it. It can be a frustrating process and the results are often disappointing.

When it comes to technology adoption and the accompanying behavior changes, we tend to follow the same approach. We make grand plans for extreme change and then have trouble sticking with them. When leaders do this, it sets up colleagues and employees for frustration and disappointment. Dieting is ineffective at producing long-term results because it is a short-term solution. The same is true of organizational change that isn't supported by metrics and a sustainment plan. There is a better way! Many people

> **"Organizational change requires adoption of new behaviors, changes in process, and most importantly, a real commitment to a long-term plan for sustaining change."**

have discovered the benefits of making meaningful and sustainable behavior changes that have a long-term impact. Organizational change requires adoption of new behaviors, changes in process, and most importantly, a real commitment to a long-term plan for sustaining change. Metrics are vital to supporting a successful transition, and they provide visibility into whether changes in clinical documentation and coding have been effective and are being sustained over time. Measuring results provides the visibility needed to identify gaps in performance in the ICD-10 adoption effort. The delta between the desired state and actual results signifies an underlying system dysfunction or lack of sustainability. Well-designed metrics allow symptoms to be identified in time to react quickly and effectively. Metrics also support the ability to diagnose causes that underlie failure. For example, performance gaps and the resulting rework stem from a variety of factors, including insufficiently documented diagnoses (provider-caused) or poor translation of well-documented diagnoses into codes (coder-caused).

> **"Well-designed metrics allow symptoms to be identified in time to react quickly and effectively."**

73

Previously, we noted that the process of restoring equilibrium is represented by a balancing feedback loop, as illustrated in Figure 10. Well-designed process indicators and performance metrics allow us to compare actual results with desired outcomes (the performance gap), allowing us to identify the appropriate intervention to bring the system back into balance (Karash, 1996).

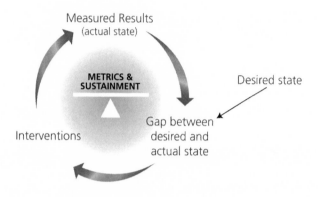

Figure 10: The Process of Using Metrics to Sustain Adoption

Positive actions to close a performance gap caused by coder inaccuracy, for example, may include enhanced coder training, workload re-balancing to address time pressures, investment in computer-assisted coding technology, and/ or initiatives to improve the provider-coder relationship. Armed with knowledge about underlying conditions that influence performance, committed healthcare leaders are better equipped to design interventions that close performance gaps, bringing desired and actual results into alignment and restoring healthy operation.

To be effective, metrics must be tailored to the needs of each provider. The needs of provider practices, community hospitals, and Integrated Delivery Networks (IDNs) vary greatly. The following metrics can be used to identify gaps in proficiency that impact not only ICD-10 adoption, but the efficiency and effectiveness of providing care:

- Coding productivity
- Coding accuracy
- Knowledge of coders in specific areas: anatomy, physiology, pathophysiology, and pharmacology
- Clinical documentation sampling
- Claims denial and rejections
- Case mix index

75

Sustaining the high level of adoption achieved through engaged leadership, education and metrics is critical to achieving proposed benefits. Providers who commit to the changes required for improved clinical documentation are more likely to achieve timely reimbursement, improved public health surveillance and improved measures of health services quality. Don't underestimate the time and resources required to optimize the transition to ICD-10.

In Figure 11, the process of using metrics to sustain adoption (as described in Figure 10) is depicted as an embedded balancing loop, which restores the system to equilibrium when performance gaps arise. Through interventions based on objective measurements, metrics and sustainment ensure that the reinforcing loops continue to move in positive directions. In our ICD-10 adoption methodology, engaged providers drive proficiency and proficiency drives the measurement and sustainment of new behaviors. The measurement of role-based knowledge and confidence indicates the ICD-10 level of proficiency throughout the

"...engaged providers drive proficiency and proficiency drives the measurement and sustainment of new behaviors."

organization. Metrics are the first indication when users fall back into old behaviors or lack the knowledge needed to perform. Lack of planning in the area of metrics and sustainment inevitably leads to steady deterioration of the progress made in preparation for October 1, 2014.

76

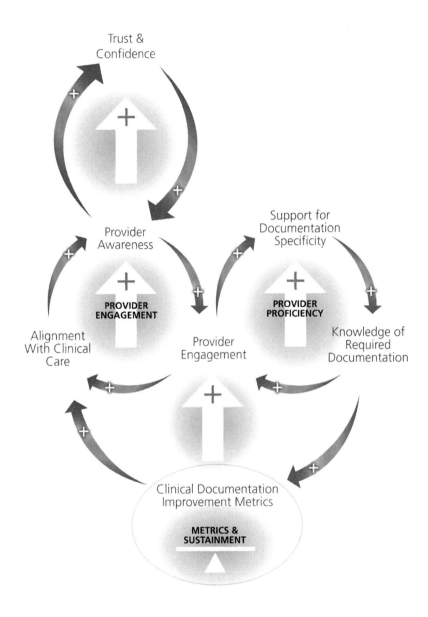

Trust &
Confidence

Provider
Awareness

Support for
Documentation
Specificity

PROVIDER
ENGAGEMENT

PROVIDER
PROFICIENCY

Alignment
With Clinical
Care

Provider
Engagement

Knowledge of
Required
Documentation

Clinical Documentation
Improvement Metrics

METRICS &
SUSTAINMENT

Figure 11: A Methodology for Provider Adoption of ICD-10

The methodology represented in Figure 11 defines the critical components of provider adoption of ICD-10 and illustrates the interdependencies among trust and confidence, engagement, proficiency and metrics. A critical aspect of the model is the identification of metrics within each area which provide a gauge for diagnosing problems that may derail or slow adoption. In Part II, we outlined the barriers most likely to impact successful reimbursement. Take a quick look at barriers specific to the physician role in Figure 6. The methodology provides a clear path for addressing each of those barriers. The real value of using a systems thinking approach is creation of a model that defines the processes, critical dependencies, and metrics to continually monitor and improve. In the case of improved clinical documentation, it moves us from a coding project to a quality of care initiative that has real meaning.

- Address potential barriers to ICD-10 adoption to create a successful transition focused on healthcare quality and accurate reimbursement of services.

- Create a plan for improving clinical documentation that garners trust and confidence among providers.

- Informed providers are engaged providers. Get informed and understand what ICD-10 means to the organization's value proposition.

79

- Develop a plan for educating providers. The success of this transition is highly dependent on both providers and coders becoming proficient in new skills and adopting new behaviors.

- Identify metrics that indicate how ICD-10 is improving the efficiency and effectiveness of providing care.

- Commit to a long-term plan for sustaining the changes that will be implemented on October 1, 2014. Remember, diets are disappointing and frustrating! Begin with a sustainable plan.

C O N C L U S I O N

• • • Engage Now • • •

Planning for the ICD-10 transition is analogous to planning for a big-bang EMR Go Live happening for everyone on October 13, 2013. Successful adoption of the new coding system requires a disciplined approach that begins long before Go Live and does not abruptly end on the Go Live date. Leaders who appreciate the magnitude

"The greater purpose is more compelling than a mandate."

of change and how it will impact key stakeholders will plan, prioritize and communicate more effectively. The greater purpose is more compelling than a mandate. Consider the intersection of efforts to adopt both an EMR and ICD-10 to create value for all stakeholders. Healthcare leaders, providers, coders and patients all benefit from improved clinical decision support and reporting on healthcare services quality.

• • • Get Moving • • •

The world of ICD-9 belonged to coders. The world of ICD-10 demands that providers become informed about the changes required for clinical documentation. Grasping the delta between ICD-9 and ICD-10 necessitates planning that addresses the barriers to a successful transition. Each stakeholder must prepare for a new role. Because the move to ICD-10 is federally mandated, compliance is not optional. Providers must begin documenting at the required specificity or risk serious financial consequences. The single greatest risk for healthcare providers preparing for ICD-10 is lack of understanding of the critical role that documentation plays in driving quality of care and reimbursement.

● ● ● Execute the Plan ● ● ●

Build trust and confidence by developing a bulletproof plan. Informed leaders must articulate the impact of ICD-10 and proactively work to align the effort with the provider's EMR adoption, clinical documentation improvement, quality reporting initiatives, and coding productivity and accuracy. Provider proficiency in clinical documentation is fundamental to adoption. ICD-10 education needs to be designed to ensure that not only are coders knowledgeable and confident in effective use of the new codes, but also that providers are knowledgeable and confident in documentation methods that drive the new coding system. This investment in people and process can begin immediately! Improvements in clinical documentation and coding accuracy provide tangible benefits today. The discipline of measuring these outcomes becomes a habit and serves the provider long after

CONCLUSION

the transition to ICD-10 is over. Continuous improvement and optimization of documentation requires a long-term commitment to education and measurement. Metrics highlight areas that need our attention and education/intervention drives improvements in those areas.

Not only will overall healthcare quality improve as a result of adopting ICD-10, but the provider who adopts early stands to establish a competitive advantage in the industry. By transforming clinical documentation prior to the ICD-10 transition, we will reap the rewards of quality reporting, accuracy of reimbursement and patient-specific clinical decision support. Engage now. Get moving. Execute on your plan!

> "...the provider who adopts early stands to establish a competitive advantage in the industry."

84

R E F E R E N C E S

American Health Information Management Association (AHIMA). (2011, March). *ICD-10-CM/PCS Transition: Planning and Preparation Checklist*. Retrieved from www.ahima.org.

American Medical Association (AMA). (2008, October 21). *AMA letter to The Honorable Michael O. Leavitt, Secretary, U.S. Department of Health and Human Services (HHS)*. http://www.ama-assn.org/resources/doc/washington/icd-10-cms-sign-on-letter-21oct2008.pdf.

Aronson, D. (1999). *Overview of Systems Thinking*. Retrieved from http://www.thinking.net/Systems_Thinking/systems_thinking.html.

Biography of Jay Forrester. (2005, November 30). Retrieved from http://www.thocp.net/biographies/forrester_jay.html on November 7, 2011.

Chavis, S. (2011, January 17). Game Changer: How ICD-10 Will Reshape Documentation Processes. *For the Record* 23(1), 14. http://www.fortherecordmag.com/archives/011711p14.shtml.

Christensen, C. (2009). *The Innovator's Prescription: A Disruptive Solution for Healthcare*. McGraw-Hill: New York.

Collins, J. (2001). *Good to Great: Why Some Companies Make the Leap... and Others Don't*. HarperCollins Publishers Inc.: New York.

Deloitte Center for Health Solutions. (2009). White paper: *ICD-10: Turning Regulatory Compliance into Strategic Advantage*. https://www.deloitte.com/assets/Dcom-UnitedStates/Local%20Assets/Documents/us_lshc_ImpactOfICD10_081409.pdf

Fred, C. (2002). *Breakaway*. Jossey-Bass: San Francisco.

Ingenix, Inc. (2008). White paper: *Preparing for ICD-10: Evaluating Approaches and Potential Pitfalls*. http://www.ingenix.com/~/media/ Ingenix/Resources/White%20Papers/Ingenix_ICD10ApproachesPit-falls_WP_1001366.pdf.

Karash, R. (1996, June/July). Coaching and Facilitating Systems Thinking. *The Systems Thinker*, 7(5). Retrieved from http:// pegasuscom.3dcartstores.com/search.asp?keyword=karash&search. x=14&search.y=6&search=GO.

Mair, N. (1999, June 30). ICD-10 – A Strategy for Hospital Implementation. *CASEMIX Quarterly*, 1 (2).

Majerowicz, A. (2011, April). Developing an ICD-10-CM/PCS Coder Training Strategy. *Journal of AHIMA*, April 2011, 58-60. http://www. himss.org/content/files/AHIMA_I10-training-plan.pdf.

Mathews, A. (2011, September 13). Walked Into a Lamppost? Hurt While Crocheting? Help Is on the Way. *The Wall Street Journal*, September 13, 2011.

Medina, J. (2008). *Brain Rules: 12 Principles for Surviving and Thriving at Work, Home and School*. Pear Press: Seattle.

Monegain, B. (2010, October 8). Pain in Limb 729.5 Doesn't Cut It in ICD-10. *Healthcare IT News*. Retrieved from http://www.healthcareitnews. com/news/pain-limb-7295-doesnt-cut-it-icd-10

Morsch, M., Johnson, G., Umbach, H., Neville, D., Delaney, B., Bradley, K., MacLeod, D. (2010, May). An ICD-10 Road Map. *Health Management Technology*. Retrieved from http://www.healthmgttech.com/ index.php/solutions/hospitals/an-icd-10-road-map.html

Natchimson Advisors, LLC. (2008, October 8). *The Impact of Implement
ing ICD-10 on Provider Practices and Clinical Laboratories: A Report to
the ICD-10 Coalition.* http://nachimsonadvisors.com/Documents/
ICD-10%20Impacts%20on%20Providers.pdf.

PBS. (1998). A Science Odyssey - People and Discoveries: *Jay Forrester 1918-*.
Retrieved from http://www.pbs.org/wgbh/aso/databank/entries/
btforr.html.

Radzicki, M. (1997). *Origin of System Dynamics. Adapted from Foundations
of System Dynamics Modeling,* prepared for the U.S. Department of
Energy's Introduction to System Dynamics: A Systems Approach to
Understanding Complex Policy Issues. Retrieved from http://www.
systemdynamics.org/DL-IntroSysDyn/origin.htm on November 7,
2011.

Senge, P. (1994, October 1). *The Fifth Discipline.* Doubleday: New York.

Schwend, G. (2011, February). Problem Lists: No Problem. *Health
Management Technology,* February 2011, 16. Retrieved from http://
www.healthmgttech.com/ebook/A1qrje/HMT1102/resources/18.htm

The authors have extensive experience conducting health-care research and organizational change. Their passion and commitment for helping leaders prepare for change led to the endeavor to understand the challenge of ICD-10 adoption, and to the findings presented here. They understand the stress created by the numerous competing priorities in healthcare today and want to ease the pain associated with the transition to ICD-10. Their greatest hope is that this publication serves as a valuable resource for embracing ICD-10, ultimately giving providers the ability to focus on patient care.

Charles L. Fred

Author

Charles Fred is the founder and CEO of The Breakaway Group. He brings a proven track record of leading significant growth in both service and enterprise software companies and has led The Breakaway Group from its initial startup to a leading position in healthcare IT adoption services.

The publication of his best-selling book *Breakaway* in 2002 initiated a "movement" by the thousands that have read it. Today, many leading universities use the text in their curricula to reinforce innovative methods for instructional technology and simulation. The eight-year research effort that ended in the publication of the book provides the foundation for The Breakaway Method™ currently used in service to healthcare providers worldwide.

Heather A. Haugen, Ph.D

Author

Dr. Heather Haugen has more than 15 years of research experience in both the academic and private sectors. She earned her doctorate in health information technology from the University of Colorado Health Sciences Center. She has an extensive and diverse professional history that includes grant writing, designing and coordinating clinical trials, research presentations and education and training for numerous healthcare providers.

Haugen's research experience ranges from weight management and metabolism to telehealth and behavior change. She is widely published in health and medical journals, including the *Journal of American Dietetic Association, Journal of the American College of Nutrition,* and the *International Journal of Obesity.* Haugen holds a faculty position with the University of Colorado Health Sciences Center's School of Medicine as the associate track director of health information technology, where she actively conducts research, mentors students and teaches courses.

Haugen is a native of Denver where she lives with her husband and daughters. She enjoys running, hiking and spending time with her family in the beautiful Rocky Mountains.

● ● ● Louann K. Reilly ● ● ●
Systems Thinking Analyst

Louann Reilly is a management professional whose focus is to advance the capability of organizations to understand and manage complex and interdependent facets of their operations. She has over 30 years of experience in industry and government, practicing and consulting in policy analysis and business process improvement, systems thinking, knowledge management, and the development of organizational cultures conducive to learning and rapid advancement. Her passion is working with dynamic organizations in adapting the way they work to changes in technology, regulation, and business culture.

Reilly is a member of the Society for Organizational Learning, a consortium of leaders from industry and academia who are pioneering learning organization theory and practice to enable large-scale change in the ways people live and work. A Phi Beta Kappa member, she has a Master of Arts degree from the Graduate School of International Studies (now the Josef Korbel School of International Studies), University of Denver and a B.A. from The Ohio State University. She has authored articles on information management and benchmarking service quality and has presented at conferences in the U.S. and Europe on information management and organizational change.

Reilly and her husband live in Denver, Colorado and are pleased to have a daughter who lives nearby. She enjoys hiking and snowshoeing in the mountains, travel, being with friends and family, and continuously learning.

The **Breakaway** Group
A Xerox Company

IMPLEMENTATION
ADOPTION A Critical Path for Success
SUSTAINMENT

The Breakaway Group delivers fast, sustainable technology adoption to healthcare organizations seeking the exceptional patient care experience.

The Breakaway Group is making a difference in healthcare by changing the way clinicians learn new workflows. By helping healthcare professionals adopt new software applications quickly and easily, providers have more time for patient care, healthcare executives see improved financial outcomes, and those leading technology implementations experience less stress.

The Breakaway Method™ incorporates an innovative learning solution housed within our **PromisePoint Community®**. We employ proven technology, processes and people that together expedite end user adoption. Our solution incorporates robust functionality for leaders and end users well before and well beyond Go Live.

To learn more about The Breakaway Group please visit
www.thebreakawaygroup.com
or contact us at
303-483-4300.

9 780984 205127